MUSEUM PUZZLE-PICTURE BOOK OF LIFE IN
ANCIENT EGYPT

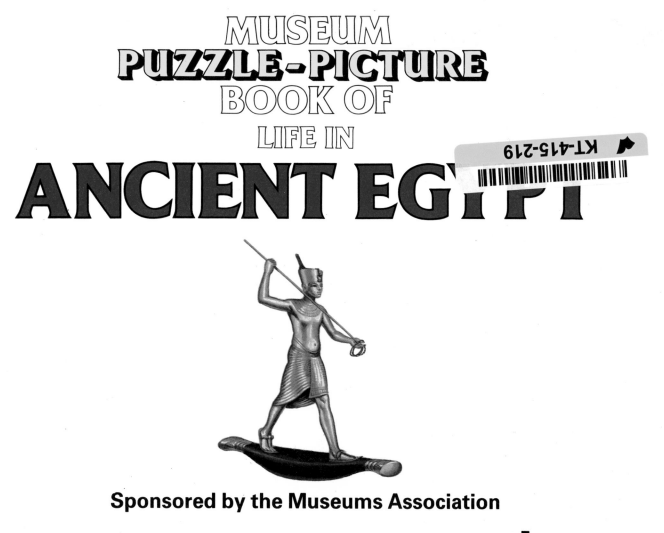

Sponsored by the Museums Association

Heritage Books & Longman

Spot the deliberate mistakes

As the river Nile flows gently by on its way to the sea, Egyptian country folk are busy about their everyday affairs. Farmers till the land; builders work on a new house; at home, the children help their mothers with the household chores.

In this picture, the artist has made eight deliberate mistakes. Can you spot them? The correct answers are on the next two pages.

COUNTRY LIFE

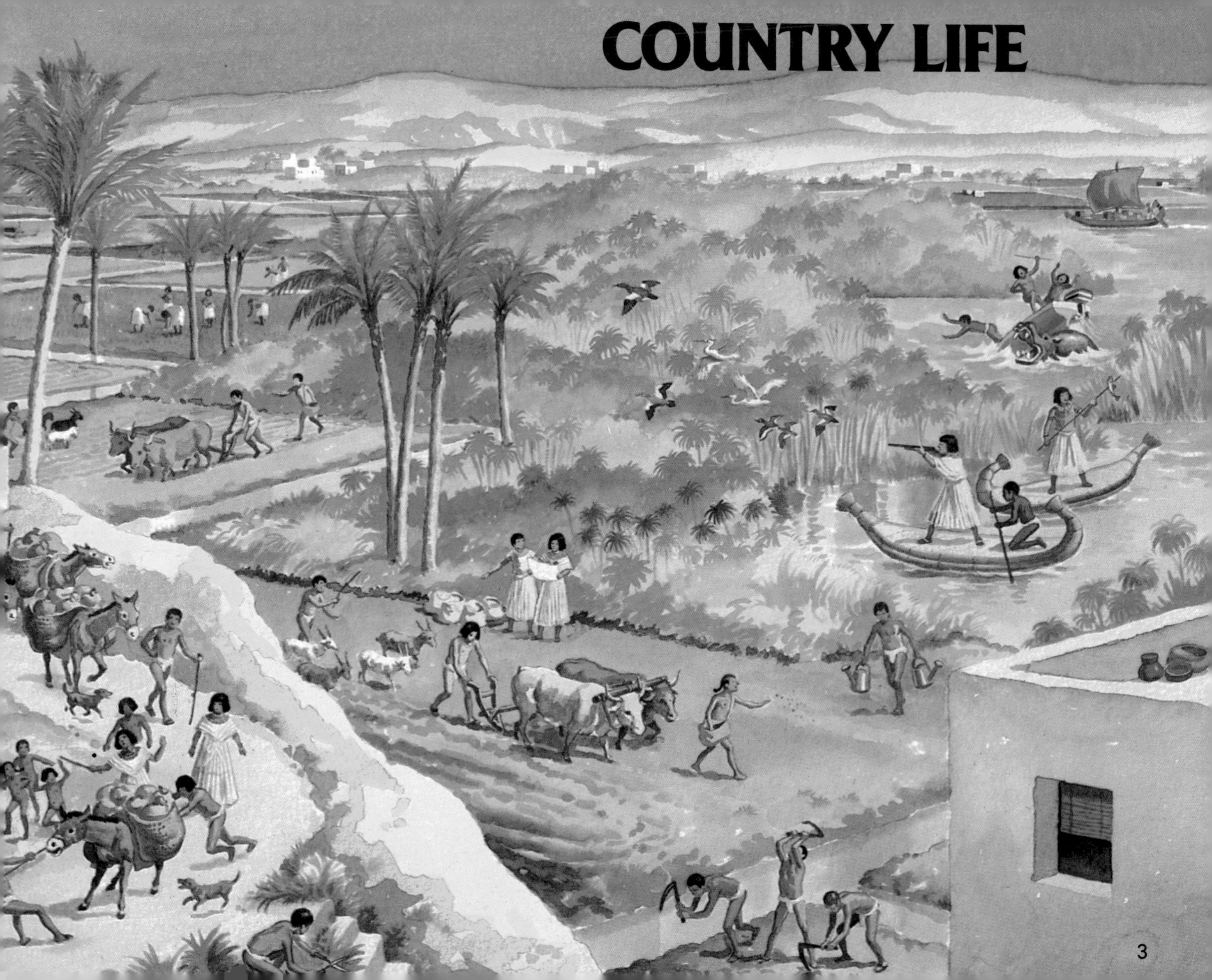

DID YOU FIND THESE THINGS?

The carpenter cutting timbers for the house is using a modern chain saw. He would have used a saw like the one in this picture. The blade would have been made of bronze. This was a mixture of copper and tin which the Egyptians worked with hammers until it was hard enough for sharp teeth to be cut along its edge. Modern saws are made of steel.

3

The boat being upset by a hippo is a modern one with an outboard motor. It would have been a reed boat. These were made with papyrus reeds tied into bundles and lashed together in the shape of a small boat. They were either paddled or rowed.

The scribe is using a modern typewriter. He would have been writing with a rush pen on a roll of paper made from the papyrus plants that grew in swamps along the Nile. The pith was taken from inside the stem, pressed into flat sheets, and left to dry in the sun. This picture shows a reed pen, pen case and inkwell and the satchel for carrying them.

2

The farm worker in the foreground is cutting corn with a pair of garden shears. He would have used a sickle with sharp flints fitted into a wooden blade. Iron was not used in Ancient Egypt and bronze was only used for special tools and weapons, so the harvest workers had to make do with sharp flints to cut their corn.

4

Beyond the palm trees a man is ploughing with a modern tractor—his plough would have been pulled by oxen. A ploughing team can be seen in the foreground. A man walks ahead scattering seed; the ploughman guides the plough; behind him a boy drives sheep over the newly turned ground to tread the seed in so that it will grow.

5

The man standing in the nearer reed boat is shooting duck with a modern shotgun. He would have used a throwing stick to knock them over. Some of these throwing sticks were shaped like an Australian boomerang and it may be that if they missed their target they would return to the thrower.

7

8

The men building the wall are using a modern concrete mixer. The Egyptians did not use concrete. They mixed Nile mud with chopped straw and poured this into wooden frames to shape it into bricks. The sun dried the mud 'brick hard'. The picture here shows how it was done.

6

The man to the right of the picture is carrying water in a modern watering-can. He would have used a weighted beam called a 'shaduf' to lift water out of the river and pour it into the irrigation channels round his fields. It hardly ever rains in Egypt and when the Nile was not in flood this was the only way to stop the fields from drying out.

A NOBLEMAN AT HOME

Spot the differences

Eight things have been changed or are missing from this picture. Can you spot them? The answers are on the next two pages.

DID YOU SPOT THESE THINGS?

1

The strings are missing from the harp. The Egyptians were very fond of music and the words of songs they sang have been found, written on tomb walls and on sheets of papyrus. We do not know what tunes they played for their music was not written down.

2

One of the bands of colour is missing from the painted column in the middle of the room. The Egyptians loved bright colours and painted their houses just as we do today. Their artists especially liked to paint pictures of birds and animals which were made to look very realistic.

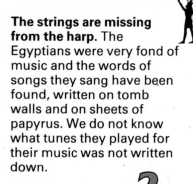

3

The bracelet is missing from the nobleman's left wrist. All Egyptians, rich or poor, loved to wear jewellery. They wore necklaces, bracelets, ear rings, arm bands and anklets. The metal used was gold but they had not discovered diamonds, rubies or sapphires.

4

The lady having her wig dressed has lost one of the bottles from the table beside her. It was a perfume bottle for one of the scented oils that Egyptian ladies liked. The little white lumps on top of the other ladies' wigs were made of perfumed animal fat. This melted slowly and ran down their heads, giving off a sweet scent.

5

One of the pieces is missing from the board game in the foreground. This game, called 'Senet', was like modern draughts but moves were made according to the throws of sticks with different number values. Egyptian children also played many games that we know—for example, leapfrog, and games with bat and ball.

7

The slave-girl dressing her mistress's wig has lost her skirt. Fine linen cloth was made from the flax plant but because it was so hot in Egypt, people needed few clothes. Most children simply went naked as did many workers, serving-girls and dancers. Rich people and officials generally preferred to 'show-off' in linen clothes, beautifully pleated.

There is a leg missing from the nobleman's chair. Egyptian craftsmen made well-designed furniture some of which looks quite modern. They used strips of leather as springs for beds and for chair seats. They had folding stools and 'put-u-up' beds, just like ours.

6

The wine jar being carried by the slave has lost its handle. The Egyptians made very fine pottery from fired clay but their best jugs and vases were made from stone. They hollowed them out with bow-drills, one man pressing down as the other worked the bow. Many examples of stoneware can be seen in museums.

8

JIGSAW PUZZLE

These eight jigsaw pieces fit somewhere into the picture. Each one contains part of something carried in the procession which King Tutankhamun will need in the next world. They will be buried in his tomb with him. See if you can spot where each one fits and say what the things they show were for. The answers are given on the next two pages.

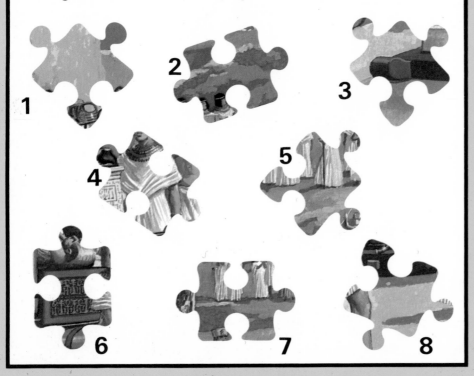

1

2

3

4

5

6

7

8

A ROYAL FUNERAL

This picture shows the funeral of King Tutankhamun whose tomb was discovered in the Valley of the Kings in 1922. The things being carried in the procession were found in the tomb when it was opened.

11

DID YOU FIND THESE THINGS?

This shows the chest at the right of the picture. We call this a 'canopic' chest and it contained the king's internal organs. They were taken out and preserved when the king's body was mummified. The process of making dead bodies into mummies is explained on pages 14 and 15.

1

This shows a chariot being carried in the procession. Six chariots were found in the tomb of Tutankhamun. This one was covered in sheet gold. The large wheels had leather tyres. There is a picture of an Egyptian chariot on the front cover.

death. Osiris was the god Egyptians believed to rule the dead and when he died, the pharoah was thought to become the spirit of Osiris.

This shows the figure of an animal on a pedestal being carried in the procession. It is a statue of Anubis, the jackal-headed god of embalmers and cemeteries. The man in the picture wearing the jackal head-dress is a priest of Anubis which is why he stands in the chief place at Tutankhamun's funeral.

This shows the 'Bed of Osiris' being carried in the procession. The sacred bed was not to be slept in. It was covered with a layer of earth in which barley was sown and when this sprouted it became a symbol of life renewed after

5 **This shows the gold statuette of Tutankhamun hunting.** Although the famous tomb was robbed of a few objects soon after the burial, it was sealed again and not disturbed for more than 3,000 years. This little statuette was one of the most beautiful things found by the archaeologists in 1922.

This shows the royal throne. It was beautifully carved with portraits of the king and his queen. Notice that the feet of the chair end in lions' claws and the tops of the legs are lions' heads. Even 3,000 years ago, the lion, king of beasts, was used as a sign of royalty.

7

6 **This shows Tutankhamun's coffin.** It is made of solid gold, encrusted with jewels. It weighs 136 kilos (300 lbs) which today makes it worth more than £1,000,000. But, of course, as one of the world's most beautiful works of art, it is priceless.

This shows the shepherd's crook carried by the new Pharoah as a sign of his duty to safeguard his people, just as a shepherd cares for his sheep. But in his other hand he carries a flail—used for threshing corn—and this was to remind his people that he had also the power to punish them. The picture here shows Tutankhamun's coffin portrait with his crook and flail.

8

THE EGYPTIAN MUMMIES

The Ancient Egyptians believed that when they died, the next world would be just like the one they knew in the Nile valley. There would be animals to hunt, games to play, music to dance and sing to. They would need weapons with which to hunt, instruments for making music, jewellery to wear, beds, chairs and all the things of everyday life. If they were rich enough, all these things were buried with them when they died so that they would be ready when the time came for them to live again. The strangest of their ideas, however, was that they would also need their earthly bodies in the next world and they took great care to preserve bodies after death so that they would be as little changed as possible. They had them mummified. The method they used sounds very gruesome to us. As priests recited the spells or read the rituals for embalming, skilled craftsmen prepared the body for mummification. First they cut the corpse open and took

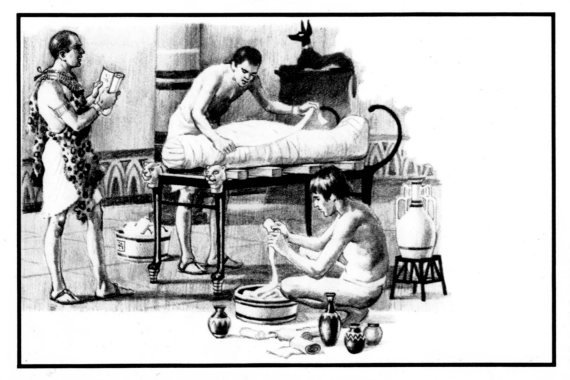

In this picture, an embalmer and his assistant are completing the bandaging of a mummy and the priest is reading the last lines of the long funerary rites. Soon the mummy will be placed within its several coffins and the burial will follow.

out all the organs—liver, kidneys, lungs and intestines. These they preserved separately. Then they removed the brain. They developed a special way of drawing the brains out of the head, through the nostrils, so that no damage was done to the skull. The heart was left in place for it was believed that this organ would have special importance when the body came to life again. The other organs were put into canopic jars or a chest, as described on page 12. The body itself was then treated with a chemical called natron which dried it out. Spices and herbs were applied to it to make it sweet and finally it was wrapped all over in fine linen bandages as the picture here shows. The likeness of the dead person was then preserved by a portrait painted on the coffin lid and this coffin was put into another coffin-like box to keep it safe. Later, in Roman times, this careful process—which took nearly three months to complete—was given up, and instead, bodies were preserved by simply dipping them in bitumen, or tar.

The name 'mummy' comes from the Arabic word 'mumiyah' which means 'bitumen'.

Only pharoahs and the richest Egyptians could afford to have their bodies mummified and buried with all their possessions in elaborate underground tombs. Ordinary folk were just buried in the ground which meant, of course, that according to Egyptian ideas, they had little chance of another life.

It is these strange beliefs, however, that have made it possible to know so much about these people who lived such pleasant lives in Ancient Egypt, for many of the things that were buried with them—for the next world—have been found and put into museums for all to see and wonder at.

The Egyptians also invented a kind of writing so that we are able to read about them in their own language, for a lot of their writing has survived. On the next page there is an Egyptian alphabet. Use it to write your name.

Tomb robbers

The tomb designers of Ancient Egypt used all kinds of tricks to foil robbers. They hid entrances behind solid masonry or built false ones that led nowhere; underground passages leading to burial chambers were blocked by huge stones lowered into place when the tomb was sealed; deep pits were dug in passageways, too wide to cross without a bridge; false passages led only to dead-ends and if at last a burial chamber was reached, robbers would still find the entrance blocked.

The Ancient Egyptians took great care to protect their treasures for use in the next world but the tomb robbers, despite all those clever tricks, found most of it. The rest is mostly on display in museums—or is it? Could there still be treasure buried in the Valley of the Kings? Archaeologists still work there. Perhaps, one day, another rich tomb will be found—but it could, of course, take another 3,000 years!

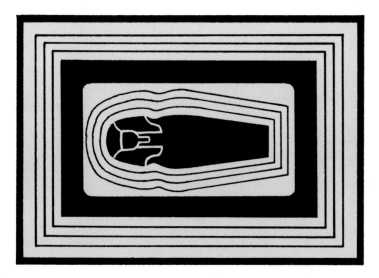

EGYPTIAN WRITING

Write your name in Hieroglyphs

The Ancient Egyptians used pictures, called 'hieroglyphs', for their alphabet. Unlike our writing, they did not use vowels—only consonants. By slightly cheating, however, you can use some of their pictures as though they stood for vowels. For example:

The vulture can stand for **A**
The arm can stand for **O**
The reed can stand for **I** or **Y**

You can see these in the table below.

There is no picture for **E** so this must be left out when you write your name in hieroglyphs. There is also no letter **L** and the Egyptians used the sign for **R** instead. For the sound **CH** in CHARLES, use the sign for **TJ**.
For the sound **J** in JOHN, use the sign for **DJ**. For example, this is how to write the names:

CHRISTOPHER

ROSEMARY

JACKIE

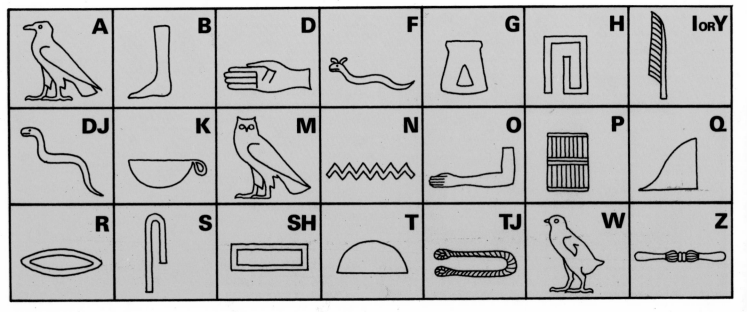

A	B	D	F	G	H	I or Y
DJ	**K**	**M**	**N**	**O**	**P**	**Q**
R	**S**	**SH**	**T**	**TJ**	**W**	**Z**